Bea and Brodies' BIG BOOK OF CREATIVITY

featuring the art of Heather McLennan

and

the words of Susan Cohen

First edition, 2022
The Wee Book Company Ltd

www.theweebookcompany.com

A catalogue record of this book is available from the British Library.

ISBN 9781913237035

Graphic design consultancy by www.colorprinz.com
Printed in Scotland by Bell & Bain Ltd, Glasgow

BECOMING CALM AND MINDFUL

Let's keep our ideas flowing
Let's keep growing more and more
Let's create the Bea and Brodie way
For there's so much more in store

Being in the present moment
Can clear our way ahead
Breathing deep and being still
Can calm our busy heads

And turn down all the noises
Of any rowdy roaring thoughts
Which can block our creativity
And tie us up in knots

So let's soar high through clear blue skies
Let's set our imaginations free
Let's continue to explore
How exciting fresh ideas can be!

AN ENCOURAGING PICTURE

Everyone needs encouragement
Yes, we need that now and then
So just let Bea and Brodie
Help you be your own cheer-leading friend!

Take a piece of paper
And draw a colourful phrase, a slogan
One that's all about you
That lifts you up when it is spoken

Be your own supporter!
Be your biggest fan!
Every day look at your drawing
And know you can, you can, you can!

You can do anything!
Your imagination has no limits!
You can open your creative mind
And plant endless ideas in it!

How does music feel in your heart?
How would smells appear?
What colours would tastes be?
What sights could you draw near?

What would feelings sound like?
What would cold say if it could talk?
Would hot go on a picnic?
Would a sour taste sit on a rock?

Would sharp be friends with soft?
Would blue sing rock and roll?
Would songs swim in the ocean
Like silver fish in a big shoal?

Could Brodie sail across the sea?
Could Bea learn to speak French?
Could a huge hot air balloon
Squeeze under a park bench?

UPSY-DOWNSY

Think all upsy-downsy
What if birds flew far below?
What if your feet floated over your head?
And the ground was where stars glowed?

What if Brodie was tiny wee?
And Bea the size of a plane?
What if balloons fell from the sky?
And lemonade rose up like rain?

What if trees grew under the sea?
And fish lived on the moon?
What if the sun fell from the sky?
And Christmas was in June?

Make your mind stand on its head
Let it see things upsy down
Let it take a helter skelter slide
To the sky, to Wacky Town!

ICE CREAM, I SCREAM!

Ice cream
I Scream
Sunbeam
Day Dream

Thinking
Blinking
Shrinking
Winking

Creating
Ice skating
Animating
Hibernating

Put different words together
Wow, what a surprise!
Just watch how new ideas
Appear before your eyes!

SCRIBBLES

Pick and trace a scribble
Onto a piece of paper
Use it to start a drawing
Oh, what a fun-filled caper!

Is it a wee buzzy bee?
Or a wiggly wriggly worm?
Is it a huge spaceship?
Or a butterfly that turns

Back into a caterpillar?
Not the other way around!
Is it a fluffy rain cloud
That falls down to the ground?

Try doing this another way
Do it with some friends
All of you get scribbling
The fun will never end!

What would life look like
Through the eyes of a wee dog?
How would you croak a happy song
If you were a leaping frog?

How would you do your homework
If you were a Highland cow?
How would you bake fairy cakes
With a big snow plough?

How would you wear a floppy hat
If you were a honeybee?
How would you go buzzing round
If you were a Christmas tree?

Try to sometimes see the world
From different points of view
It can make things round you
Seem exciting and brand new!

A DIFFERENT FORM

If you weren't a human being
What would you choose to be?
Fish? Animal? Plant? Insect?
A tulip? A honey bee?

Would you be a sunflower?
Or a killer whale?
Would you be a cabbage?
Or a tiny snail?

Would you be a red deer
With horns upon your head?
Who never used them to fight
But used them to love instead?

Such endless possibilities
Imagining a different form
The wackier the better
Have a creative brainstorm!

DRAW WITH YOUR EYES

Look at something near you
Then reach out for a pen
Draw without once looking down
And see what happens then!

You start drawing just by sight
Drawing every angle, every line
You're drawing blind, no peeking
You're letting your creative instinct shine!

Do this over and over
And your confidence will rise
As you draw with pen and paper
But only with your eyes!

DRAW WITH YOUR MIND

Look at something near you
A chair, a tin of beans
Take in every little detail
Make sure everything is seen

Now take yourself away
And from memory, just draw
Everything in your mind's eye
Everything you saw

The more you start to do this
The more you'll start to see
You'll look slowly and more calmly
You'll let your creativity just be!

SAME PICTURE THREE TIMES

Paint or sketch a subject
Once, twice, three times
Every time oh-so different
Let your creativity shine!

Have you drawn big Brodie
With big bananas for coo horns?
Have you given Bea a tutu?
Well, watch how she transforms

From a bee into a dancer
Full of style and grace
Doing leaps and pirouettes
With a happy little face

Changing just one subject
In the most unexpected ways
Breathes new life into art
And brightens up your days!

WHAT? IF? HOW?

What if you listened to music
And drew every little sound?
What if you felt warm water
Imagined it wrapping round

Your fingers just like smooth silk
What would that look like to you?
Would it have a colour?
Pink or green or blue?

What if you saw butterflies
Who were best friends with the wind?
What emotions would they feel?
Imagine! Where to begin?

How to turn this into art?
Would you make a sketch or two?
Would you put all this to music?
Just think what you could do!

MOVE SPEAK THINK!

Instead of drinking orange juice
You could have a cup of tea
Instead of singing a wee song
You could buzz around like Bea

You could walk a different route to school
To meet a friend or to the shops
Instead of walking to the bus
You could do funny bunny hops

You could pretend to be Brodie
Walking round on hooves
You could coo-coo like the pigeons
Who perch on top of roofs

Try doing things differently
Move speak think in brand new ways
Step away from your old habits
It will transform your days!

GOOD MORNING, FREEWRITING!

One way to explore your mind
Is to pick up a pen
And write and write and write and write
No matter how, no matter when!

Write anything that comes to mind
No need for grammar or spelling
Your words will take you with them
Where? There will be no telling!

It can be best to do this when you rise
From your sleepy bed
It's when your dreams are buzz-buzzing round
Your dozy drowsy head

Focus on your words flowing
In wonderful new ways
Just leave a pen by your bedside
And every morning write write away!

BE A **4-4-4** SUPERHERO!

Stand strong and stretch both arms up
Feet apart, stand straight and tall
Raise your eyes up to the sky
Yes, you can conquer all!

Breathe in for a count of four
Your superhero's breath begins!
Imagine you are flying
Hair blowing in the wind!

Keep your breath down in your belly
Hold for a count to four
Then blow out counting four again
Do it over – a wee bit more!

You can do anything you want
Yes, you know you can!
You can be Superwoman
You can be Superman!

BIG BELLY BREATHS

Rest both your hands on your belly
Breathe nice and slow and deep
Feel your hands move with your body
It's just like when you sleep

You'll start to feel all peaceful
Your body knows just what to do
Your mind will find its own way
Down a quiet avenue

That leads to a peaceful calm place
Where you can watch your thoughts
Come and go and jump around
But not tie you up in knots

Keep doing your big belly breaths
They'll clear your busy mind
Leaving worries, niggles, troubles
A long long way behind.

Dear you,

Welcome to Bea and Brodie's Big Book of Creativity!

Journey through this workbook - for ages 5 to 105 - and watch how Bea and Brodie have come up with all sorts of wild and wonderful things to help make your creative ideas z-z-z-zing!

First, clear and calm your mind - you'll find that every time you do this, the easier it gets!

Do this by going to 'Big Belly Breaths' or 'Be A 4-4-4 Superhero' and following the easy peasy breathing exercises. This workbook is full of surprises! Or relax and listen to Bea and Brodie's CREATIVITY BUBBLE - find it at www.theweebookcompany.com/audiobooks and use the password BUBBLY. Luvverly!

Or how about doing all three? Woo hoo! Whee hee! You can just let go and b-r-e-a-t-h-e, setting any jumbly tumbly thoughts or worries free to just l-e-a-v-e. Take your time, there's no hurry!

Second, leaf through the pages of this workbook and try out some of Bea and Brodie's weird and wacky creative ways! Which ones will you choose to do today? How will you do them in your own special way?

Can't wait to see!

with love,
Bea and Brodie x